GW00731785

Cumbria
WEATHER

Your Complete Guide

by

PETER JOHNSON

ISBN 978-0-9549480-16

Printed in Great Britain by
Stramongate Press, Kendal, Cumbria

Published by CINDERBARROW PUBLISHING

About the author

An Associate Fellow of the Royal Meteorological Society, Peter Johnson has lived in Cumbria for many years, having been brought up at Greenodd, in the south of the county. He has always had a life-long interest in weather and climate, and has had work published by 'Weather', the journal of the above Society.

Apart from having written articles for diverse publications ranging from 'Which' magazine, the 'Times Educational Supplement' and Airline In-flight Magazines he is also the author of a very successful guide-book: 'M6 Cumbria – England's Scenic Motorway – Short Journey Breaks', also published by Cinderbarrow Publishing.

As regards the 'hot topic' of man-made Global Warming, he feels that the jury is still out!

He is married with three daughters, and has four grandchildren.

He lives in Levens.

'It is commonly observed, that when two Englishmen meet, their first talk is of the weather'

Samuel Johnson (1612 – 1680)

For Rebecca, Sam, Alex and Jamie

Cumbria's Weather – Introduction

Cumbria has a unique geography, with a knot of central mountains being at the hub of a wheel, and the main valleys with their lakes arranged as its spokes. With the sea to the west, and the Pennine range to the east, depending upon which direction the wind blows, coupled with the season of the year, the scene is set for a bewildering variety of possibilities as regards the weather.

There are numerous excellent guide-books to the county. However, the author makes the claim that this publication is unique in giving both the visitor and resident precise and valuable weather information. Armed with this local knowledge, gathered over many years by the writer, the reader has a head-start in making the very best of what the weather has to offer. It is designed to be used in conjunction with practically all guidebooks to the area.

It may be obvious that a visit to a waterfall during a drought is not a good idea, but this book should make sure that the reader will get the most out of the day, whatever the weather may bring. In addition, it contains much information as regards Cumbria's weather and climate, not readily available elsewhere.

The Lake District has a reputation for being excessively wet. Although Borrowdale receives roughly five times the rainfall of London, it does NOT have five times as many wet days, but when it rains, it rains!

It is often asked by the visitor – when is the best time to visit Cumbria? The question cannot really be answered, as all seasons have their advantages and disadvantages. It is, however, possible to have an enjoyable holiday at any time of the year, whatever the weather has in store.

Part One of the book contains much valuable information as regards weather-related phenomena, and also historical weather events. This has mostly been gathered over many years by the author. In particular, some of the rainfall and snow-cover data are the result of personal observations. It must be remembered however, that although the long-term average rainfall for each month indicates the likelihood of dry or wet weather in any particular season, it is only an *average*. Remember with our fickle climate, *average* is the key word – nothing is guaranteed! An average can only be considered meaningful when calculated over very many years. It is well to remember the cautionary tale of a fatal disease, with an average age at death of 45 years. Only 2 cases of the disease had ever been recorded, at 85 years and 5 years!

Part Two of the book considers what weather can be expected in each of the four seasons, together with suggestions for how to make the most of the seasonal changes. Obviously some venues have their attractions at any time of the year, but others are only at their best during certain seasons, or under particular weather conditions.

Also to be found is guidance as to how to find the most up-to-the-minute weather information, along with comments concerning the possible effects of climate change on Cumbria's weather.

Part Three of the book considers how the weather and climate of Cumbria has impacted on the work of both writers and artists who for many years have been drawn to the region. This is such a wide-ranging subject that the author has chosen just one writer and one artist to develop this theme. The topic could in itself easily become the basis of an entire book.

Colour Photographs: These photographs have been carefully selected to illustrate various points mentioned in the text.

Acknowledgements will be found on page 55.

Detailed explanations concerning each illustration will be found on pages 58 onwards. Several are rare, and a few are unique. Some prints are available from websites.

PART ONE
Cumbria's weather, past and present

Facts you never knew about Cumbria's climate:

- At the peak of the last Ice Age, a huge dome of ice covered all the mountains excepting the top few hundred feet of the western fells. This exposed area became the region of frost-shattered rocks familiar to every walker. Such peaks poking above ice caps are common in Greenland and Antarctica, and are known as nunataks.

- There is indisputable evidence that in the late Bronze Age and the early Iron Age the climate was warmer, by at least 2°C and in addition less windy than at the present time. The remains left by such early inhabitants of the region are chiefly in the form of hut circles. A glance at any Ordnance Survey map of Cumbria will show that they are generally found between about 800 feet (250 metres), and 1,400 feet (430 metres) above sea level. Many are in what today would be considered as very exposed positions.

  A prime example is to be found at Devoke Water, in the south west of the county, where as many as up to 400 hut circles are to be found, 800 to 900 feet up (approximately 300 metres) and wide open to Atlantic gales. If by the quirk of some planning aberration a new settlement were to be built there, the unfortunate inhabitants would without doubt be quickly blown away!

- Moved to the same latitude south of the equator, Cumbria would be practically uninhabitable, with glaciers, and icebergs off-shore. It would be roughly in the position of South Georgia, with average summer temperatures of about 6°C instead of 16°C.

- Rather more than 2,000 years after the end of the last Ice Age, when the climate was warmer than today, the glaciers suddenly returned for a period of about 500 years. They then quickly disappeared as rapidly as they had appeared. Moraines marking the ends of these glaciers are common in the area, and can be seen at the head of Mickleden, Langdale, and also at the bottom of the Kirkstone Pass road near Patterdale, as well as on Dunmail Raise. It is thought that the sudden drop in temperature was caused by a failure of the Gulf Stream. *Watch this space!*

- About 5 to 6,000 years ago, the climate was at least 2°C warmer than at present – large tree trunks from this period can be found buried on Cross Fell well over 2,000 feet (600 metres) above sea level. Such trees will not now grow at this height.

- At that time, because of all the melting ice, sea level was higher than today. The old shore-line, even with sea caves, is best seen in the Grange and Lyth Valley area in the south of the county.

- In both the Roman Period and also the Middle Ages, the climate was warm enough to grow grapes. At the present time, though grapes will set in warm, sunny and sheltered locations, in most years they will not ripen. Similarly, outdoor tomatoes, except in favoured locations, are hit or miss. Almost always, unfortunately, from the writer's experience, a miss!

- The Arctic Char (sometimes spelt Charr), a fish living chiefly in the cold water at the bottom of some of the deepest lakes, is closely related to the salmon, but has lost its ability to migrate.

- Damsons, which get their name from Damascus from where they originally came, have been grown for several hundred years in the Lyth valley, the climate and soil particularly suiting them.

- Under present climatic conditions, the absolute extreme temperature range that can be expected lies between about -22°C and +35°C (-6°F and 95°F)

- Ambleside recorded -6°F in 1940, with a deep snow-cover.

- An annual drop of only 2°C or 3°C in the average temperature would result in permanent snowbeds on the fells re-appearing, and in most years crop failures would be widespread.

- Carbon dioxide gas dissolves in rainwater to form a weak acid, carbonic acid. Fears that the acid rain so formed would damage trees, because of the heavy rainfall in Cumbria, have proved to be completely unfounded.

- Over the last ten thousand years or so that have passed since the last Ice Age, this acid rain that has been falling has had a marked effect on the limestone areas. About 12 inches (30 cm) of the rock has dissolved away. The result is that impervious rocks left stranded by the retreating glaciers are left perched on 1 foot pillars of limestone that have been protected from Cumbria's weather over many centuries. Such erratics are best seen at Norber, just outside the county near Kirkby Lonsdale.

Historical Weather Events

There must have been countless major storms, floods, heat waves, blizzards and tidal surges over the centuries which have gone completely unrecorded. There is one scar on the landscape which is almost certainly the result of a violent thunderstorm hundreds of years ago. This is known as

Drygrove Gill:
This lies on the east side of the Kentmere valley, high up opposite the reservoir. This deep ravine cannot have been eroded by a stream, as it starts close to the summit of the fell, and so lacks a catchment area. It has the same V-shaped form as a similar ravine on Pendle Hill in Lancashire, known to have been formed as the result of a violent storm about 400 years ago. As regards this gash on the fellside above Kentmere, with an easterly wind in winter, it tends to collect the snow and can be seen as a long white streak high up on the fell long after all other snow has melted.

The Scafell Area:
This high and rugged mountainous area is well used to stormy weather. If the major lakes of the Lake District are regarded as the spokes of a wheel, then this region can be seen as the hub. Winds and storms from all directions converge here, so 200 inches of precipitation per annum (both rain and snow) is not out of the ordinary.

In 1958 it was the scene of a truly remarkable storm. This occurred on the afternoon and evening of August 10th, though there were further violent storms on September 6th and also on October 6th. Several miles away, in the Langdale valley, rain was measured falling, at the edge of the storm area, at more than 2 inches per hour. 2 inches in 24 hours would be considered a very wet day with localised flooding!

It was estimated at the time that at the storm centre, about 3,000 feet (950 metres) above sea level, more than 6 inches of rain fell per hour.

The result was that enormous torrents of water were unleashed, which gouged out huge channels, permanently altering the landscape. Massive new scree slopes were formed below Scafell Crag, with many boulders weighing over 50 tonnes crashing down the mountain, even as far as fields in Eskdale, thousands of feet below. With the passage of time, the rock-falls have blended in, and only by reference to photographs of the area taken previous to 1958 can the enormous scale of erosion produced by this single storm be truly appreciated.

The Origin of St. Bees:

A long tradition going back to the Middle Ages implicates the peculiarities of Cumbrian weather as being involved as regards the settlement of St. Bees in the extreme west of the county. It is said that St. Bega, the leader of a group of nuns from Ireland, was wrecked upon the coast and requested land from the local Lord on which to build a House of Prayer. He agreed, (no doubt with a knowing smile on his face!), as he made the condition that the nuns could have as much land as was covered with snow on the next day, which was Midsummer's Day. Surprise, surprise, next morning the coastal strip of land for a few miles was covered with snow!

The legend certainly rings true, as heavy showers confined to a narrow coastal strip are a characteristic feature of winds from the NNW. As for snow lying in midsummer on low ground, this is entirely possible. The Log Book of Levens School, near the coast in the south of the county, records a snowstorm in the village on June 16th, 1869. It also records that snow was seen to be still lying on the mountains on June 21st, the longest day of the year. The most recent occurrence of snow on low ground in June was in 1975.

Perhaps if the Lord in question had listened to Radio Cumbria's weather forecast, he would not have made so rash a promise!

Freezing of the Lakes:

It is relatively common for the smaller, shallower lakes and tarns to freeze to some extent during the winter. With a cold snap, sheltered bays and inlets soon develop a skin of 'cat ice', but it is much rarer for Windermere, the largest lake, to form ice thick enough for skating, or to bear the weight of a car. In some years extensive areas have frozen (1929 and 1979), while in 1895 and again in 1963 it froze sufficiently thickly to allow skating. On the last occasion, the author can remember walking across frozen Derwentwater. On Windermere, a narrow passage was kept clear of ice as much as possible by running the ferry continuously. In some sunless bays, the ice reached 1 metre in thickness. Derwentwater was again partly frozen in January 2009.

During the 1895 freeze-up, special excursion trains ran from London to Lakeside via the branch line from Ulverston, which is now sadly only a rump of its former self. The only part still functioning is the short stretch from Haverthwaite to Lakeside.

Photographs from the time show good skating conditions; better than in 1963, as then the ice was rather rough, with melted and re-frozen snow. Ice-floes also formed extensively in river estuaries in 1895 and 1963, and more recently in 1979, and to a small extent in 2009.

Snowstorms:

In low-lying coastal areas of the county heavy and persistent snowfalls are uncommon, because of the effects of the salt air combined with the relative warmth of the Irish Sea. However, they have occurred, as in the 1940's. Because of the war and the threat of invasion, they are not well documented, but it is known there were 8 foot drifts in the Barrow area, with a general depth of up to 2 feet. Buses and trains were reported to be completely buried. More recently (in February 1996), a level fall of more than a foot also occurred in coastal areas to the south of the county.

Heavy snow in Pennine areas is much more common, with Hartside Pass between Penrith and Alston usually closed for several days each year. 1947, 1963 and 1979 were particularly severe. It is very strange that severe winters have practically always occurred in odd-numbered years – if you have an explanation for this, please let the author know!

Mountain Snow:

On the highest Lake District Fells, and also on the Pennines, a fresh snow cover has been observed in every month of the year, except August (that is, as far as the author is aware) – though Daniel Defoe did report snow in August in parts of Yorkshire. Both the months of June and September produce the odd day's temporary new covering about once in ten years. The first few days of June 1975 produced a covering down to 1,500 feet (about 450 metres), and on September 20th 1919 heavy snow covered all land down to only 800 feet (about 250 metres) above sea level.

Other instances recorded are:
- July 3rd 1802, Dorothy Wordsworth mentions 'snow on the mountain tops'.
- July 11th 1888 the snowline was reported to be halfway down Skiddaw.
- July 1938 Helvellyn was reported to be snow-capped after heavy overnight rain.

As regards the Lake District fells, but not the Pennines, 1951 was by far the snowiest winter of the 20th Century. Winds were mainly from the West and North West, giving heavy precipitation in the Lake District, but again not on the Pennines. Huge drifts built up, which lasted well into July on all the eastern slopes.

In 1979, giant drifts built up on the western slopes of the Pennines, as this time the snow-bearing winds came from the east. In that year, it was still possible to ski on the west side of Cross Fell in the first week of July, the last snow melting in mid-August. It was believed in the eighteenth century that the snow remained throughout the year, and accounts exist of expeditions to find such 'eternal' snow' – they were not successful!

An 'average' figure for complete snow-cover for Cross Fell and Helvellyn of about 100 days per year must be taken as a very rough approximation.

There does seem to be some slight evidence that snow was more persistent in the early nineteenth century, as the scientist John Dalton made a regular visit to Helvellyn in the first week of July.

He records in his diary that he found snow remaining 'in the usual place, about a quarter mile north of the summit'.

The 'usual place' is Brown Cove. Snow is sometimes to be found there in early June, but not nowadays in July.

The Sea:
There are numerous instances of the sea producing coastal flooding, as a consequence of a high spring tide and storm-force winds. In the south of the county, on the night of the 31st January 1983, the stone built pier at Arnside was reduced to rubble by a violent storm. It was rebuilt, and re-opened on 12th April, 1984.

At the other end of Cumbria, the viaduct that carried a railway between England and Scotland over the Solway to Annan, suffered a similar fate. It was built in 1869 and was rather more than a mile in length. It was several times severely damaged by the freezing of the sea and in 1881 ice floes caused the structure to become unsafe. It was repaired, but was eventually dismantled in 1934.

Flooding caused by heavy rainfall:
Despite Cumbria's reputation for heavy rainfall, because of its topography, severe flooding is rare in the central area because of the rapid run-off. On the outskirts, Cockermouth and Kendal have in the past suffered repeated floods, but flood prevention schemes have greatly lessened this danger.

Flood marker stones recording past inundations are to be found by the river Kent in Kendal and also in the grounds of Levens Hall.

The Carlisle Floods, 9th January 2005:
These unprecedented floods (at least since the 1860's), with 9 inches of rain falling, were caused by all the rivers in the area overflowing their banks. Two people drowned in their homes, while cars floated down the streets and helicopters were used to rescue stranded victims. On

January 8th, a windspeed of 128 mph was measured on the not-far-distant Dun Fell.

Since these floods occurred, the Authorities have been working hard on various flood prevention schemes, to minimise the effects of any future flooding.

The 'Irruption' of Solway Moss:
Solway Moss, northeast of Carlisle, was a raised peat bog. During the night of November the 16th, 1771, after persistent heavy rain, it began to move slowly, and completely buried over 20 farmhouses, in a morass of 500 acres which was 30 feet deep. No lives, other than that of cattle and sheep, were lost as it is recorded that the inhabitants fled in time, with, or sometimes without, their night-clothes!

Such raised peat bogs have declined significantly in numbers over recent years. Those remaining are regarded as 'SSSI', i.e. 'Sites of Special Scientific Interest'.

Weather Related Phenomena

The Bore at Arnside:
No, this is not your uncle Fred regaling you with the same joke for the tenth time after his fifth pint, but is a rare natural phenomenon, *which is critically dependent on the weather conditions prevailing.*

Morecambe Bay has one of the highest tidal ranges in the world, up to about a maximum of 34 feet (11 metres) depending on the state of the weather. If a deep low-pressure area is centred over the Bay, a storm-surge is automatically produced. The Bay narrows and becomes more shallow as it forms the estuary of the river Kent at Arnside.

Sometimes, the incoming tide can form a wave travelling upstream, commonly described as 'faster than a horse can gallop'. Favourable conditions for the formation of a bore are a high tide, a following south wind and also low air pressure. The form of the wave also depends crucially upon the narrowness or otherwise of the channels just below the railway viaduct at Arnside, which change on a daily basis. A warning siren is sounded in plenty of time, which can be heard up to 5 miles or more away, to make sure no one is left in danger out on the sands.

If you are lucky, you will see a wave sufficiently developed to be ridden by canoeists, but frequently, with apparently everything in its favour, the wave almost fails to materialise, and is disappointing.

Details of the time of high tide are to be found on Arnside Pier, and they are also published on Fridays in the 'Westmorland Gazette'. Don't forget that the Bore, if it materialises, will arrive at least 2 hours before this time.

The word 'Bore' is derived from Old Norse, and just means 'wave'. In older written accounts of the phenomenon the word 'Aegir' is sometimes used. This is the name the Vikings gave to the god of the sea. Both words, along with many local place-names show a close connection with the Norsemen who originally settled in the area, arriving via the Isle of Man.

The Arnside area is very popular for its gentle hill and coastal walks. Note the apparently missing pier of the viaduct. This is not storm damage, but was deliberately omitted to allow the bridge to open so that sailing vessels could reach the open sea from the then port of Milnthorpe upstream. With the coming of the railway, the whole region has long since silted up.

How to get there: take the A591 (A6) south from Kendal to Milnthorpe, turning left just beyond the 'Barn Shop', (which has won several National Awards) follow the A590 Barrow road for about 300 yards and turn left to Milnthorpe. Turn right here for Arnside.

Walking across Morecambe Bay:
On no account attempt to do this without a guide. Remember, the depth of water at high tide can reach more than 10 metres, or about 32 feet and it is quite impossible to outrun the Bore.

There are records going back to the twelfth century listing fatalities, and there was even a Coroner's inquiry in 1346, into the great loss of life occurring on crossing the sands. Most churchyards surrounding the Bay have their complement of tombstones inscribed with the legend 'drowned crossing the sands'.

You may well ask why anyone ever bothered to cross the sands with its attendant dangers. The answer lies in the geography of the region. Before the coming of the railway, the only relatively safe means of reaching the Cartmel peninsula and also the Furness peninsula was a very long detour. This went via Kendal, then by the south end of Lake Windermere, thus avoiding not only the sands but several practically impassable bogs.

However, with the Queen's Official Guide, the approximately 8 mile walk from Arnside to Kents Bank near Grange is certain to be a memorable day out. Walks take place from April to October, and again, *are critically dependent on the weather conditions*. They are advertised locally. For further information, see 'Between the Tides' by Cedric Robinson who at the time of writing is the 25th guide since 1501. Guides, whose names are now lost to us, are known to have existed long before this date.

These walkers are glad to be reaching Kent's Bank at the end of their 7 mile hike across the Bay from Arnside.

A few hours later, their route would have been covered by about 30 feet/10 metres of water!

Mountain Weather

Unfortunately, every year weather-related accidents, sometimes fatal, occur on the fells. It is essential to appreciate the difference between conditions in the valleys and those on the fell-tops.

Many videos and TV programmes can give a completely misleading impression, in that they fail to convey the difference in climate between the valleys and the summits.

A knowledge of what to expect is essential both for enjoyment and also for personal safety.

Here is an actual example:

5th March, 2008
Grasmere Village: Light showers, sunny periods. Maximum temperature; +10.1°C or just over 50°F. NW wind, 8 mph.
Helvellyn Summit: Heavy snow with blizzard conditions. Maximum temperature; - 0.2°C or just below the freezing point. NW wind, 40 mph gusts, i.e. up to gale force.

This means that it was a pleasant day, with daffodils blowing in the spring sunshine in the village, while winter still reigned supreme on the mountain summits; full winter equipment including ice-axes and crampons, being essential.

Taking the wind-chill factor into account, on the tops the temperature would have felt more like minus 9°C or about minus 16°F in a gale-force wind. Unless you are an experienced walker, it is advisable to keep your excursions to the lower hills, except for the summer-time. Rain and snowfall are much higher on the fells than in the valleys, and in addition the wind is generally far stronger.

Gales are frequent on the fells. They are common in all seasons except summer, and gusts of over 100 mph are nothing unusual. One of the highest gusts officially recorded was 133 mph on Dun Fell, east of Penrith. This particular fell is easily identified, as its summit is crowned with a 'radar golf ball', clearly visible to the east of the Eden Valley.

Ian McVittie skiing on Cross Fell, *July* 1979

Lakeside, Windermere, July 2008 & February 1895

Tidal Bore, River Kent

Long Meg Pillar

Long Meg sunset on the shortest day of the year

Windswept tree

After sunset

Coastal thunderstorms moving south

Glacier termini, Dunmail Raise (above) & Langdale (below)

It would be extremely difficult and expensive to have an automated weather station on the summit of such a popular mountain as Helvellyn. It would certainly lead to a loss of 'wildness' at 3,117 feet (950 metres) above sea level, even though there is a memorial there recording the landing of a small plane on its summit!

Consequently, there is at the time of writing a service whereby from December to April, observers are employed by the National Park on a daily basis to climb to the summit and take readings, which are then relayed to the 'Weatherline'.

Wind-chill:
This is a measure of what the temperature feels like to the human body, as opposed to what the thermometer indicates. It was revised from a rather unsatisfactory older measure and was standardised in November 2001.

A knowledge of this is absolutely vital to all walkers.

Hypothermia can develop easily even in the summer if you are not dressed properly for conditions on the high fells. The rate of fall of temperature with height on the Cumbrian fells varies enormously with the weather conditions. On rare occasions, it is actually warmer on the summits than in the valleys. Oddly enough, this happens most frequently in the winter, with the valleys being frost and fog-bound, while on the tops the sun shines in a clear blue sky. However, for most of the time it is colder, sometimes very much colder, on the summits. In extreme cases, usually in the Spring, the temperature difference between the valleys and the tops can be 10°C or even greater. Under average weather conditions, it is between 6°C and 7°C.

Wind-chill greatly adds to the perceived much lower temperature on the higher hills. Even when it is relatively calm at valley level, the windspeed increases very rapidly with increasing height.

On rather rare occasions national weather forecasts on both radio and television do refer to wind chill, but are best ignored, as they take no account of the very rapid increase of this factor with height above sea level.

The best way to counteract its effects is to take plenty of warm clothing if venturing on the high fells. Several thin layers are far more effective than taking one thick layer.

Even in summer, your rucksack should always contain a pair of gloves.

This book is not the place to consider the excellent volunteer Mountain Rescue organisation that exists in Cumbria. Although they deal with fractures caused by falls and walkers lost in the mist, they certainly confirm that wind chill and its attendant possibility of life-threatening hypothermia is Public Enemy Number One.

It is not generally appreciated that even when the true temperature is several degrees above the freezing point, with a strong wind blowing, the wind chill effect means that the perceived temperature is actually below freezing.

Conversely, without a wind blowing, and the sun shining, it is possible to be in shirt-sleeves on a sunny day in February, even though the temperature is not that far above freezing. However, if the sun goes in and the wind rises, even if the true temperature remains the same, the wind chill effect will soon be very noticeable.

Your Rough Guide to Wind-chill

A mild winter's day:

	light breeze	strong breeze	gale
Wind Speed (mph)	5	20	40
Actual Temperature (°C)	10	10	10
What it feels like (°C)	9	6	5

A cool winter's day:

	light breeze	strong breeze	gale
Wind Speed (mph)	5	20	40
Actual Temperature (°C)	5	5	5
What it feels like (°C)	4	0	-3

The Brocken Spectre:

This can sometimes be seen by the walker under the right conditions. The observer must be above an even layer of mist or cloud, with a clear sky above. The sun must be at a very low angle, under which circumstances a giant shadow of the walker, complete with halo, is projected onto the cloud. It can usually only be seen early in the morning or late in the evening. However, in mid-winter with the sun only about 12 degrees above the horizon even at midday, it can be observed at any time of the day.

It takes its name from the highest peak in the Harz mountains in Germany, the 'spectre' being part of German folklore.

Long Meg and her Daughters:

This prehistoric monument is included here as it illustrates how the changing seasons, with their changing weather, were important to the inhabitants of Cumbria more than 5,300 years ago. Latest estimates indicate that it is one of the oldest stone circles in the district, probably older than the pyramids in Egypt.

The shortest day of the year is clearly indicated by the 14 feet-high stone, 'Long Meg,' which stands well outside the circle of stones. Unlike the other stones, it is of local sandstone, and on it can be seen enigmatic 'cup and ring' markings. On the shortest day, the sun appears to set directly on top of it, as seen from the centre of the ring. (The points of the compass are clearly indicated by large stones)

Try counting the stones – it is said that you will never get the same answer twice!

Best time to visit: mid-November, with mists and drizzle, when *'the chill rain begins at shut of eve'* (Keats). Even better, go there on December 21st, and pray for a fine afternoon!

We shall never know all its secrets, but it is quite clear that at least one of its purposes was to determine the winter solstice. It would then have been a simple matter to count forward from that date in order to determine how long it would be before the weather could be expected to improve. It was in a sense the local inhabitants' first attempt at weather forecasting, the start of a long road leading eventually to weather satellites.

How to get there: Long Meg lies to the northeast of Penrith, and like many other prehistoric stone circles, lies on an elevated site with wide horizons. Take the Alston road from Penrith, turn left at Langwathby, on to Little Salkeld, (here there is an old water mill which grinds its own flour, not to be missed), then turn right up the hill, where there is a signpost.

The Helm Wind:

This phenomenon, the only wind with a specific name in Cumbria, occurs on the western slopes of the Pennines in the Eden valley, almost always in the spring months.

When a strong, steady NE wind blows, a line of clouds forms above the Cross Fell range, with a smooth, curved top. (Hence the name 'Helm', as it resembles the shape of a helmet). The sky is then clear to the west for a mile or so, and then can be seen a line of clouds parallel to the Pennines; stationary but in rotation. This is known as the 'Bar'.

The result is a cold, severe and gusty wind blowing down the western slopes of the fells and into the Eden Valley. It can blow at severe gale force, while only a mile or two away the air is relatively calm.

It can be unpleasant and irritating – certainly not the place to go for a picnic.

How to explain it?

Make your own 'DIY' version of the phenomenon. Place a smooth rock (the Pennines) in a steadily-flowing stream, gently sloping on the upstream side (east), but steeply sloping on the downstream side (west). See how the water rushes madly down the downstream side, (western side of the Pennines into the Eden valley) while further downstream an eddy (the Bar) appears at a fixed distance.

Substitute air for water, and you have your explanation!

In effect, the Helm Wind produces a 'standing wave' in the atmosphere. Exactly the same effect occurs with the 'Levanter' at the Rock of Gibraltar.

Cross Fell, at 2,930 ft / 893 metres above sea-level is the highest point of the Pennines. It is considerably higher than many well-known Lake District fells, such as the Langdale Pikes or Coniston Old Man.

It has always had a reputation for wild weather. During the Middle Ages, it was supposedly the haunt of demons, and was always given a wide berth. Many sources state that its name was changed , sometime in the medieval period, to Cross Fell after a Mass was held on its summit by some local monks.

Whatever the truth of this, wild weather is certainly common in the area. Hartside Pass, just to the north of the mountain, is frequently blocked by snow during the winter months.

Cross Fell is also crossed by the long-distance footpath, known as the Pennine Way. This stretches from Edale in Derbyshire to Kirk Yetholm in Scotland.

During the 'Little Ice-age' of the 17th Century it was reported that snow sometimes remained there unmelted throughout the year. One report states that 'it had remained unmelted together for seven years'.

At such a distance in time, these statements are impossible to verify, but are certainly within the bounds of possibility.

Your Questions Answered

Will it Rain?

Cumbria has a reputation for being a wet region, but just how wet is it? Coastal regions, as well as the Eden valley have the lowest rainfall, with average annual figures in the mid 30's (inches) (700 to 800 mm).

The lowlands and areas near the sea frequently remain dry all day, while the fells experience passing showers.

A small area in the Scafell / Great End central mountainous region probably exceeds 200 inches on average per year, as do parts of Snowdonia in Wales and also Glenn Garry in the Western Highlands of Scotland.

The highest gauge in Cumbria, at the aptly-named Sprinkling Tarn, has recorded an average annual figure of about 196 inches (5,000 mm). At present, it is said to hold the British record for the most rain recorded in a year (1954) at a truly staggering 257 inches (over 6,500 mm). This is **over 6.5 metres or more than 21 feet!**

The wettest inhabited place in Cumbria, indeed in England, is Seathwaite in Borrowdale with an annual average fall of over 130 inches (3,300 mm). Kendal, at about 55 inches (1,400 mm), and Keswick at about 58 inches (1,500 mm) have much more modest totals.

In October 1967, the wettest for any month for over 100 years, 29 inches of rain fell at Langdale in 29 days.

In the summer, the most reliable dry period is the first 10 days of June, and in the winter the most unsettled period tends to be the 10 days starting on December 20th.

Local weather lore asserts that if you can see Coniston Old Man, it is going to rain, but if you cannot see it, it is raining already. This saying is universal, however and is often applied to Ben Nevis, Snowdon or any other peaks one cares to name.

There is a huge variation in annual totals of rainfall, from just above 30 inches (760 mm) on the coast to 200 inches (5,000 mm) only about 15 miles distant in the Scafell region. This six-fold increase does *not* mean that there are six times as many wet days in the hills as on the coast.

Days with measurable rain, though varying greatly from year to year, are roughly about 200 on the coast, to about 236 at Seathwaite, in the heart of the mountains. The three extra wet days per month are the result of showers over the fells, whilst coastal regions remain dry. Thunderstorms tend to form in hilly regions, and can result in heavy, but at the same time, localised rainfall. For comparison, the driest parts of Essex have an average annual rainfall of about 20 inches (510 mm), falling on 150 days.

Annual Pattern of Rainfall
Numbers show the % of annual rainfall for each month

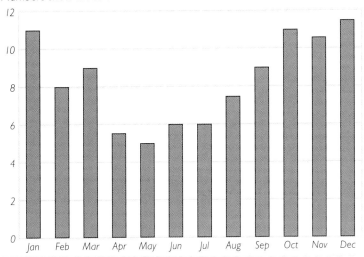

The above chart, derived from more than 30 years of readings, clearly shows that October, November, December and January each account for more than 10% of the annual rainfall. The results are slightly skewed because February has 10% fewer days than March.

The April/May period is generally the driest along with the first weeks of June. As the year progresses, both the rainfall and cloudiness steadily increase. Remember that these are the average figures: there have been occasions when February has been rainless as the result of persistent easterly winds.

Although, on average, December is the wettest month of the years, sometimes August, as many visitors will have experienced, can run it a very close second.

Is it possible to forecast the future from past weather records?

Up to a point, the answer is, rather surprisingly, yes. Annual rainfall records do tend to show a saw-tooth pattern, with a drier year being followed by a wetter year and vice-versa. On this basis, it should be drier on average in 2009, 2011 and 2013 while wetter years can be expected in 2010, 2012 and 2014 etc.

Over the last 30 years, odd-numbered years have averaged as much as 10% less rainfall than even-numbered years, though, as always, there are the exceptions!

There were no *truly* severe winters between 1895 and 1947, that is, a gap of 52 years, and the next one was 1963, a gap of only 16 years. Another is almost due, and keeping to the pattern of only occurring in odd numbered years, 2009 or 2011 seem to be strong candidates.

Since the previous paragraph was written, this forecast has been borne out by the much colder than average winter of 2009. Perhaps the Met. Office forecast of a warmer and wetter winter than actually occurred could have been the result of a computer virus?

Droughts

It all depends what is meant by the term 'drought'!

Though dry periods, with no rain for three or four weeks do occur, they are uncommon. True droughts, with the land burnt brown, no rain for months and vegetation dying, do not occur. There have been years with lower-than-average rainfall throughout, but for a calendar month to pass completely rainless is a very rare event.

It did, however happen in Seathwaite, the wettest inhabited place in England in February 1932 when no rain whatever was recorded.

There have been dry periods when the level of Haweswater has fallen so low that the remains of the village of Mardale have reappeared. This is caused by not so much the lack of rain, as by water being abstracted by the Water Authorities.

Will it Thunder?

Thunder is not as common as in many other parts of the United Kingdom. It is not evenly distributed in Cumbria, with three distinct areas more prone to storms than the rest of the county.

The first region most likely to be affected by storms is the central mountainous area. Here, on hot days in July and August towering cumulo-nimbus clouds can build up during the day, which by late afternoon become fully-fledged thunderstorms. This usually happens with generally light winds, as if a strong wind or gale is blowing on the fell-tops, the storm does not have time to develop before it becomes dissipated.

This accounts for the commonly observed fact that when such storms do occur, they happen in the late afternoon and are generally slow moving. Intense downpours can then occur at one place, while only a matter of just a few hundred yards away, the ground remains dry.

The second region that experiences more than its fair share of storms is the Kirkby Lonsdale area, where, under certain weather conditions, south westerly winds blowing off Morecambe Bay form a line of storms which travel up the Lune Valley towards the Pennines, while nearby regions remain relatively clear.

The third region to be affected, oddly enough, is the western coastal fringe of the county. Here thunder is experienced during the winter and early spring months, rather than during the summer. It can even occur with hail, snow and sleet falling. It does not happen as a prolonged storm over an hour or so, but as just one or two peals of thunder and flashes of lightning. It is formed by the passage of a cold front over the relatively 'warm' sea causing vigorous convection which in turn forms cummulo-nimbus clouds over the coast, and for a short distance inland.

Will it be Sunny?

The answer to this question largely depends upon two factors - the time of year and also the wind direction. In mid-winter, even on a clear day, the sun will not put in an appearance much before 9 o'clock in the morning, and it will have set by about half past 3 in the afternoon. Tables of the times of sunrise and sunset published in the newspapers are of little value, because they take no account of the hilly and mountainous nature of central Cumbria.

In former times, many farmhouses were built facing north east in the lee of hills, for protection against the prevailing south westerly winds. They were certainly not erected to enjoy the view. Consequently, in the winter months many see little direct sunlight. There are a few which are completely in shadow from mid-November to mid-February, examples being under Melbreak, near Crummock Water.

Around midsummer, the sun rises about half past four in the morning, and does not set until shortly before ten o'clock in the evening. This means that for a short period about the midsummer solstice the sky is never truly dark.

The possible hours of direct sunlight therefore vary from about six hours in the winter to about seventeen hours in the summer.

Because clear weather is more likely in April, May and the first half of June, these are the days most likely to have long hours of sunlight. July and August, typically considered to be summer months and also being the chief holiday months, usually have much less sunshine, as they are normally wetter and cloudier.

Hours of sunshine, in common with inches of rain, vary enormously over relatively short distances when averaged throughout the year. Unlike rainfall, precise figures are difficult to quote, owing to a lack of sunshine recorders. The older instruments, consisting of a glass ball focussing the sunlight onto a piece of paper, so burning a trace in it, are being superseded by electronic recorders, but these are giving results at variance with the older method.

For the purpose of comparison, parts of the south coast of England can have more than 2,000 hours of sunlight annually, the coast of Cumbria roughly 1,500 hours and the central fells are lucky if they top the 1,000 hours mark.

So where do you go to find the sun?

As a general rule, if an east wind is blowing, go west. Under these conditions, the Pennines tend to be cloudy, as do the eastern Lake District fells, while the west of the county and the coast are usually more or less cloud-free. Conversely, with wind and rain coming from the west, the cloud often breaks over Penrith and the Eden valley. Here it can be pleasantly warm and sunny, while only a few miles to the west it is cool and wet.

Penrith also benefits from the 'föhn' effect. As air moves from the west over the fells, it is forced upwards and loses its moisture. It then descends in the direction of the Eden valley and is compressed. In the same way that the air in a bicycle pump heats up as it is compressed, the same effect is felt in Penrith and the Eden valley. This area then becomes warmer by a degree or two than it would otherwise be, if the fells to the west did not exist. Under certain conditions, this area can be sunnier, drier and warmer than anywhere else in Cumbria.

In the Alps, with the mountains being higher, the föhn wind has correspondingly greater consequences. When this wind blows, both the rates of suicide, road traffic accidents and murder rise. The author has no figures for Penrith!

Most of the coastal regions of the county are usually sunnier than inland, though the peculiar geography of the south of the county is the culprit for an unexpected lack of sunshine in parts of the area. The fell Black Combe, west of the Furness peninsula, is the southerly outpost of the Lake District, separated from the main mountain mass. On occasions, being high enough to produce a constant line of clouds which stream eastwards from its summit, when a west wind is blowing it critically affects hours of sunlight in the direction of Ulverston, Grange and Arnside. The net result can be clear blue sky to the south, but places a little to the north can be cloudy all day, while less than a mile away there is uninterrupted sunshine.

Recently there has been concern about excess levels of UV radiation causing cataracts and skin cancer. Daily levels are quoted on local television. Fortunately in Cumbria there is little to worry about, when compared with Australasia and America. High levels are very infrequent, and do not last for any length of time.

With concern growing over fossil fuel sources of energy, it has been claimed that solar panels could be a viable alternative energy source. Is this the case in Cumbria, given its highly variable weather? The answer is a qualified 'yes'. As is the case with wind energy, many wild and unsubstantiated claims are still to be heard. The facts are that during the summer months solar panels can provide a substantial part of domestic hot water requirements in the sunnier areas of Cumbria. They are not an economic proposition in the central areas. Photovoltaic panels that convert solar energy directly into electricity are definitely non-starters at the present time for domestic use, even in the sunniest regions of Cumbria. The surface area required to produce useful amounts of electricity is so large that the cost is completely uneconomic.

One exception to this can be seen on Coniston Water, where a solar-powered launch now operates successfully during the summer months.

It is possible that the amount of direct sunlight in Cumbria is now being affected by man's activities. It just so happens that very busy transatlantic air routes to and from both America and Canada pass directly over the centre of Cumbria in a north-south direction. When atmospheric conditions are favourable, the sky can become criss-crossed with vapour trails that spread out and only slowly dissipate. They eventually form a thin veil of cirrus clouds. Whether the clouds reflect sunlight, and produce a cooling effect, or whether they act like a blanket and keep the planet warm is a moot point. One thing is certain – they do reduce the intensity of sunlight reaching the ground.

On clear, starlit nights the winking navigation lights of passing aircraft can be seen from any elevated ground away from street lights. There is always one, and sometimes there are up to ten aircraft visible at any instant.

Will it be Windy?

Cumbria, lying on the western seaboard of England, is exposed to weather systems tracking eastwards from the Atlantic. Its climate is considerably windier than that of the south and east of the UK.

As with rainfall, there is a definite yearly pattern as regards the likelihood of strong winds. The summer months are the least windy, though gales have occurred at sometime or other in all months of the year. The so-called 'Equinoctial gales' are not a regular feature of the weather on September 21st, but there is a marked tendency in autumn for the average strength of the wind to increase. This reflects the growing temperature difference between the Arctic and the still relatively warm Irish Sea.

Winter and early spring are the times when strong winds or gales are most likely to be experienced.

Visitors from both Europe and America are often perplexed by the fact that the hills and mountains of Cumbria are not tree-covered to the summits. This is chiefly a consequence of the incessant wind at high altitude. At lower altitudes, over-grazing by sheep plays a part. Low summer temperatures, rather than low winter temperatures also inhibit growth. In a few places which are well-sheltered small, stunted trees will grow up to 2,000 feet (610metres) above sea level. This is, in effect, the absolute tree-line.

All walkers on the high fells will know that even when just a light breeze is blowing in the valleys, on the tops an incessant strong or even gale-force wind will be experienced. High winds can be much more dangerous than is commonly appreciated. Doubling of windspeed results, not in twice the energy being exerted, but in four times as much coming into play.

Just how strong can the wind be?

For exposed coastal locations, such as St. Bees Head or Walney, winds of over 90 mph in storm conditions are sometimes experienced. Above 3,000 feet (900 metres) on the high summits, windspeeds tend to be higher, at times over 100 mph. There are no instruments at the time of writing for measurements of windspeeds on the high fells of the central Lake District, but Dun Fell, at 2,735 feet (834 metres) in the Pennines, has a weather station that, amongst other things, monitors the strength of the wind. The highest figure it has measured so far is 138 mph. This can definitely be considered as rather windy, as gale force is generally to be reckoned as 40 mph.

Windy weather does have its advantages. More wind means less fog. Dense fog, that sometimes afflicts particularly the Vale of York and other parts of the country, is infrequent. Valley fogs tend to occur in the autumn and winter under anticyclonic conditions, but are readily dissipated by even a light breeze. In windless conditions, the lakes create their own fog-banks, sometimes only a hundred or so feet deep. Because of this, lakeshore roads round many of the lakes can have very poor visibility, while elsewhere is clear and sunny.

Even in very windy weather, fog can be a hazard. Commonly described as hill fog, it is in effect low cloud. If the cloud base comes down to only a few hundred feet, then many roads can be affected.

At times high winds can be more than just a nuisance, they can be destructive. In 1908 a train was blown off the viaduct over the river Leven estuary near Ulverston in a violent gale (without loss of life), and on several occasions in recent years many high-sided vehicles have been blown off the higher parts of the M6 motorway. Even a large wind turbine was reduced to a tangled mass of wreckage in the Caldbeck area. Many thousands of trees were also blown down in a storm in the winter of 2005.

At first sight it would be expected that in such a windy climate, windmills would have been used for grinding corn. However, with high rainfall and plenty of streams watermills were a far better option from the Middle Ages onwards.

A few were erected in windy coastal areas, such as Walney though they have long since fallen into disuse.

Huge wind turbines have now been erected off-shore in the Walney area and also in the Solway Firth to take advantage of the free source of energy. Many smaller developments inland are also being proposed or developed. Pros and cons are hotly debated, but unfortunately in very cold winter weather when demand for energy is at its peak, the days are usually very calm and frosty. Under these conditions, the turbine blades hang motionless!

A very large development of wind turbines proposed at Whinash, near Tebay was eventually refused planning permission after a long and expensive Public Inquiry. The grounds for this refusal were that the damage it would cause to the scenic environment and also its negative effects on tourism would far outweigh any benefit from the electricity generated.

Hydro-electricity is greatly under developed, with just a few plants in operation. With the high rainfall of Cumbria, more such plants would be visually less intrusive and far more reliable than wind turbines.

The huge energy of the tides remains as yet untapped, though there are proposals for a barrage across Morecambe Bay to utilise this energy source. It is said that the monks of St. Bees got there first, with their tidal –operated corn mill, commemorated in the local place-name 'Sea Mill Lane'.

Will there be Snow on the Fells?

Under present climatic conditions, it is possible to see new snow any time between September and June, and old snow remaining in July and August.

The following data refer to the summit of Fairfield, 2,864 feet (873 metres) above sea level, near Ambleside. They show that the average

Fairfield snow-cover days

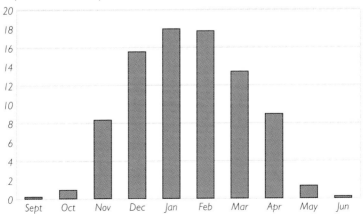

number of days in the year that the summit has carried a covering over the last decade is 85. The figures vary wildly from 117 in 1995/1996, to as little as 53 in 2001/2002. Drifts last much longer, normally into May on the north-eastern side of the mountain. As can be seen from the chart, the average number of days in the month varies from less than 1 for June and September, to about 18 in January and February

How far can you see?

The answer here depends on the source of the air mass and the wind direction. Experience shows that by far the best visibility occurs when the wind is from the unpolluted Arctic, i.e. a northerly. All other wind directions produce some degree of cloudiness, along with haze.

The most distant views are not always from the highest mountains. Also, some statements to be found in guidebooks as to what can be seen are occasionally somewhat dubious.

Black Combe: - this almost 2,000 feet (600 metres) high outlying fell in the south of the county, near Millom, lays claim to our most-distant view.

As Wordsworth wrote in 1813, referring to the view from its summit:

'The amplest range of unobstructed prospect may be seen, that British ground commands'.

The view is said to extend to Jack Hill and also Talk o' the Hill, near Hanley and Stoke-on-Trent in Staffordshire. The distance as the crow flies is approximately 110 miles.

Snowdonia in Wales, about 90 miles away can certainly be seen, and with binoculars individual peaks can be identified. This part of North Wales can also be seen from Coniston Old Man, Bowfell and the Scafell Range, being about 100 miles distant.

As would be expected, the Isle of Man at about 45 miles is clearly visible, any land to the north of it being Galloway in Scotland. Contrary to what is sometimes claimed, the Mountains of Mourne in Ireland are definitely NOT to be seen, the line of sight being blocked by Snaefell on the Isle of Man.

Wordsworth comments again as regards the view- could that be

'... the line of Erin's coast?'

but he does add a question mark. If it can be seen, it is to the south of the Isle of Man, and is about 120 miles distant.

Looking in the other direction, Black Combe can clearly be observed, low on the horizon to the north, from beaches on Anglesey and also from the Wirral peninsula, over the Mersey from Liverpool.

Skiddaw: - unlike the high fells Helvellyn and Scafell, where the line of sight is blocked by the Isle of Man, the Mountains of Mourne in Ireland can be seen in line with the northern tip of the Isle-of-Man. They are about 120 miles distant. Criffel, near Dumfries in Scotland is easily seen just the other side of the Solway Firth in Scotland, with Merrick, 2,766 feet (843 metres), also easily visible at 60 miles to the north-west.

More contentiously, there have been claims that the 2,766 feet (843 metres) peak of Goat Fell on the Isle of Arran, at about 100 miles, and also the 3,200 feet (974 metres) peak of Ben Lomond north of Glasgow, nearly 120 miles away, are part of the panorama. This is theoretically possible but rather doubtful!

Cross Fell: - as this, the highest peak of the Pennines at 2,930 feet (893 metres) is situated roughly mid-way between the west and east coasts, it is not surprising that it is claimed to be possible to see both coasts at the same time. The Solway, at about 40 miles is easily visible to the west-north-west, but the nearest part of the east coast, south of Newcastle and about 45 miles distant, is more problematical, as there is some high moorland intervening. The jury is out on this one, unless you know better!

It must be remembered that favourable weather conditions giving views up to 100 miles are rare. However, at times there is a mirage effect over the sea, and the mountains of North Wales can look much nearer than they actually are. When this happens, they can be seen from low ground or even from sea level from the south of the county.

It is often the case that the view can be crystal clear in one direction, but in the opposite direction it is obscured by cloud and mist to only a few feet.

The absolute limit at which an identifiable geographical feature under the most favourable weather conditions can be seen, seems to be about 120 miles.

This topograph was erected by Heversham Parish Council on Heversham Head, to celebrate the Millennium. A much older one, erected in the nineteenth century on Hampsfell near Grange, clearly indicates the mountains of Snowdonia.

Top 10 Tips to make
the most of the weather:

- *Ignore BBC and ITV weather forecasts* – in recent years both have been 'dumbed down', are too general, far too brief, frequently lack isobars and often make no mention of the Lake District. 'The North' can mean anywhere from Liverpool to the North of Scotland.

- A detailed, local and largely accurate forecast is broadcast on Radio Cumbria at 8.30 am. It gives fell-top conditions, and is light years ahead of any other radio forecast! A detailed local service is also provided by the National Park.

- Parking charges are in many places excessive, and many a trip can be ruined by rushing back to the car early because the time has expired on the parking ticket.

- To solve the problem, avoid venues where parking is difficult and expensive. For members of the National Trust, free parking is available at most of their venues.

- If the weather looks good, go for the outdoors. Leave your trip to the shops, art galleries, restaurants and pubs for the wet weather.

- Whatever the season, ALWAYS take some food and drink with you – unlike urban areas, if that café you visited on a previous visit is closed, the next one open could be ten miles away.

- Take more rather than less outdoor clothing with you, and remember that high quality walking boots are a very sound investment.

- So you are going to take some superb photographs with your new digital camera? Always take a spare battery!

- Early morning and late evening, with a low sun and long shadows, tend to produce the best photos.

- Walking poles have become increasingly popular with all ages, and no longer carry connotations of being 'over the hill'. In a different sense you will be over the hill more quickly by using them, as they have been proved to increase walking efficiency by more than 20%.

PART TWO
Cumbria's changing seasons

For each of the four seasons suggestions are made as regards particular places or activities which should give the most enjoyment, *depending upon the weather*. Obviously they are not exhaustive.

There is some dispute as to when the seasons start and finish. There are sometimes days that could belong to any month of the year. It is possible for the minimum temperature on the shortest day of the year, in midwinter to be higher than that occurring on the longest day of the year, in midsummer. A clear June night can easily produce a temperature of 5°C, while during a wet, cloudy and mild night in December the temperature may remain close to 10°C.

Anyone who has visited countries near the equator, where seasons do not exist (apart from wet and dry periods) will realise that seasonal differences in the weather are much to be appreciated. The only downside for places situated at the latitude of Cumbria, between 54°N and 55°N are the short hours of winter daylight. Carlisle lies at approximately the same latitude as Ketchikan in Alaska. In midsummer the sun sets at about 10 minutes to ten, but in midwinter it sets about 20 minutes past three in the afternoon.

Adopted in this book is the system used by the Meteorological Office, that is:

Spring: March, April, May
Summer: June, July, August
Autumn: September, October, November
Winter: December, January, February

SPRING: *March 1st to May 31st*

General comments: This period of the year is frequently the least wet, with April on average being the driest month of the year. In addition, with the equinox on the 21st or the 22nd of March, at this time the length of the day increases very rapidly.

In most years, easterly winds are at their most common, which is generally a cold direction, but fortunately the Pennine range to the east protects the Lake District from the persistent fogs (sea-fret or haar) that plague the eastern part of England.

Pleasantly warm sunny days can occur, but in early spring snow flurries can affect the eastern fells, while the west remains dry. Nights can be cool, with the latest air frost at sea level to be expected about the middle of May. A brief touch of frost on the ground is not unusual in early June, more especially in upland districts away from the milder coastal areas, for example Shap, and also parts of the Eden Valley.

Mid May can sometimes also bring the last new snowfall to the high fells, though old drifts frequently remain high up in north-eastern gullies. Here they are protected from both sun and rain. The first day with a maximum temperature of over 20°C can be expected sometime in early May, much more rarely in April – there is an enormous year-on-year variability. Spring frosts can be very severe, causing damage to fruit tree blossom – on April 5th, 1919 minus 15°C was recorded near Penrith. However, on occasions, if the rest of the summer is cloudy and cool, the hottest day of the year can occur in May.

Springtime in Cumbria tends to proceed in fits and starts, so that the best time to visit in order to see daffodils, bluebells or the Lyth valley damson blossom varies from year to year. Hedgerows and trees are also coming into leaf at this time, bringing new life to the countryside, along with the appearance of newborn lambs, frolicking in the fields. It is also one of the windiest times of the year.

Spring arrives first in the Barrow and Millom area, and then spreads slowly north and east, to reach the high Pennines in the Alston area about two or even more weeks later.

What to expect weatherwise
Unless a Scandinavian anticyclone develops, giving a steady period of east winds, in springtime the weather is at its most changeable of the year.

The temperature difference between the valleys and the fell-tops is also at its most noticeable.

N & NW winds – excellent visibility; mornings tending to be drier than afternoons. Frosty nights. Showery days, rather than continuous rain. A stream of clouds with heavy showers often forms running down the coast from St. Bees to Barrow. It then passes through the 'Cheshire Gap' and can sometimes be traced as far as London. Inland, the skies remain clear and sunny.

E, NE & SE winds – rather gusty, and in general rather hazy visibility. Generally dry to the west, light showers to the east, sometimes of snow in the early part of the season. Cold out of the sun, otherwise pleasantly warm later in the season.

W & SW winds – most likely to bring rain or drizzle, with poor visibility; however this is the warmest direction.

Suggestions to make the most of a SPRING day out:

This is the time when woodland wild flowers are at their best. There are endless possibilities throughout the region, wherever there are native woodlands of oak, ash or birch to see wild daffodils and bluebells, but avoid areas of pine as these suppress the daylight and the undergrowth is generally sterile.

Now is the time that Stately Homes and Castles, mostly closed for the winter, open their doors. Many have fine displays of spring flowers in adjacent semi–natural orchards or paddocks.

As a visit to any local Art Gallery will quickly show, spring, along with autumn, is one of the most popular seasons for the aspiring painter.

With the rapidly lengthening hours of daylight walking on the lower fells in fine weather cannot be beaten, but unless you are experienced, leave the high fells alone!

Don't neglect the coast. With an east wind, although inland it may be dull and cloudy, Walney with its extensive seascapes is almost certainly sunny, while Fleswick Bay near St.Bees Head is completely sheltered under these weather conditions.

Being one of the windiest times of the year, a visit to Arnside to see the Bore can make a fascinating trip. This is also the time of the year that the Helm Wind tends to blow into the Eden Valley.

In mid-April 'Damson Day' takes place in the Lyth Valley in the south of the county. It is aimed to coincide with the blossom of the fruit trees, which grow there extensively. Check the precise date, as it varies slightly from year to year. This is an event with a strong local and unusual flavour.

SUMMER: *June 1st to August 31st*

Best time to visit: *First* half of June

General comments: Though a popular period to visit Cumbria, it has its own peculiar disadvantages weatherwise. On occasions, August is very wet, and can be the wettest month of the year. Nevertheless, June, and especially early June, has a reputation for being dry, warm and sunny. Frequently, later in the month, there is an abrupt change in the weather to cooler, windy and showery weather (known to meteorologists as the 'European Monsoon'). Also, towards the end of the month is seen the last of the bright fresh green new foliage, a rather dull uniform green taking over.

On average, July sees the hottest day of the year. This can be expected to be perhaps 27°C. Rather rarely 30°C may just be reached, but in a cool summer 25°C will not be exceeded.

Small snow-drifts can sometimes be found remaining on the highest fells in early June.

As Wordsworth wrote, in his poem 'Fidelity' concerning the slopes of Helvellyn, above Red Tarn:

  'It was a Cove, a huge Recess, that keeps, till June, December's snow'.

Heat waves and droughts sometimes occur, but it is not common for the water in the lakes to be warm enough for any length of time for comfortable swimming. Only the surface waters warm up, while in the deepest parts of the larger lakes the temperature is only about 4°C even in the summer. As regards the sea, there is a lack of safe beaches, though St Bees can be recommended as probably being the best during the rare heat wave – but always be aware of the rip tides.

Though regarded as a summer month, August can be expected to be slightly cooler than July. In some years, the last week can be distinctly autumnal.

Of the three summer months, June has the huge advantage of long hours of daylight. For about a fortnight around the longest day of the year (June 21st or June 22nd), especially when the weather is clear, the sky never gets truly dark. This is the time to make long excursions without fear of being benighted. There is also a local tradition of climbing Helvellyn at night in order to see the sunrise on the longest day of the year.

Aspiring photographers and artists take note: in July and August, (though not in June), the light frequently has a rather 'flat' quality, with short and indistinct shadows, and the countryside can take on a sombre dull green quality – this is not the best time of year for those particular activities.

Thunder is much less common than in other parts of the country, but is most likely in July and August – if it threatens, keep off the fells!

What to expect weatherwise:

At this time of the year, the chance of a calm day is at its highest. Winds from any direction are generally much lighter than in other seasons of the year. The chance of a gale is at its minimum in July. This is the time for sailing and canoeing, as well as taking a cruise on the numerous steamers. Uncomfortably hot and humid weather, though thankfully rare, is most likely at the end of July and the start of August.

A bonus of Cumbria's summer climate is that in general air-conditioning, which is very wasteful of energy, is completely unnecessary.

N & NW winds – excellent visibility, coolish but bright weather. Showery days rather than continuous rain. Excellent weather for all outdoor activities.

E, NE & SE winds – poor visibility, cool in June, but can be hot and sultry in the other two months.

Generally dry to the W, NE & E but sometimes a possibility of thunder from other directions.

W & SW winds – most likely to bring warm rain or drizzle, with poor visibility. (Note: August in particular can produce the occasional very wet day).

Suggestions to make the most of a SUMMER day out:

Unless the weather is very wet, give the waterfalls a miss. Make the most of the long hours of daylight. This is the time for longer and more strenuous walks or excursions, as with it being school holiday time, popular attractions can become very crowded.

There are many rewarding less accessible venues, where crowds and traffic problems can in general be avoided. These destinations tend to be on the fringe of the area.

Possibilities include:

Morecambe Bay – when both the tide and weather conditions are favourable, it is possible to walk across the northern part of Morecambe Bay in the south of the county – DO NOT ATTEMPT THIS WITHOUT A GUIDE.

Walney – 10 mile long island off the coast near Barrow-in-Furness. Wide horizons, seascapes and views of Piel Castle; in addition a bird sanctuary. To refer to Walney Island is incorrect, as the –ey- means 'island' – from Old Norse. It was named by the Vikings. Locals always refer to it as 'Walney'.

Haverigg Beach and Black Combe – windswept shore and an easily-climbed 600 metre high fell, which claims to have the most extensive views in England. *Can those really be the Mountains of Mourne in Ireland?*

Gosforth Cross – North from Black Combe, this Viking cross stands in the churchyard, where its ornate carvings have withstood the rain, snow and gales for well over 1,000 years. The sandstone is much more eroded on the south west side than on the north east side, clearly showing that South-west winds have been prevalent for many centuries. It is a mere teenager though, when compared with Bewcastle Cross, at the opposite end of the county, and a new-born babe when compared with Long Meg! This prehistoric stone calendar near Penrith had already marked the shortest day of the year for several thousand years, as the Viking warriors struggled to get the Gosforth Cross upright.

St. Bees – attractive beach, walks to the cliff-top of St. Bees Head with views to the Galloway coast of Scotland and also the Isle of Man (and again, could that be Ireland in the far distance?)

Solway shore – atmospheric memorial at the spot, with extensive wide views to Scotland, where Edward 1st, (otherwise known as Longshanks, as he was over 6 feet 2 inches tall) died on the way to 'hammer' the Scots. Yes, he's the one who built all those castles in Wales, his other nickname being 'Hammer of the Scots'.

Bewcastle – the long trip here is certainly worth it if you would like to see what is claimed to be the oldest sundial in the British Isles. A cross stands in the churchyard which itself is within the bounds of a 1,900 year old Roman Fort. Enigmatic runic inscriptions, several as yet defying translation, adorn the cross. A strange checkerboard pattern adds an air of mystery. Unfortunately, sometime during the last 1,200 years the sundial on the south side of the cross has lost its *gnomon*. (Pub Quiz members please note!).

Alston – this 1,000 feet above sea level small market town is approached over high moorland roads, with wide horizons.

Sedbergh – though now in Cumbria, typical Dales scenery, and now well-established as a 'Book Town', and home to a premier Art and Craft Gallery at Farfield Mill.

AUTUMN: *September 1st to November 30th*

Best time to visit: Middle part of October

General comments: This season is similar to Spring in that it can advance in fits and starts. The first subtle hints of its approach are sometimes evident as soon as the latter part of August, with high-lying bracken showing streaks of brown, while down in the valley it still remains green. Horse-chestnut trees are usually the first to show shades of yellow and brown, while oak trees retain their leaves well into December.

In many years, September can behave almost as a summer month, with blue skies and several days exceeding 20°C. Around the equinox, (21st or 22nd of the month), winds increase in strength, the days shorten rapidly and the change in colour of the leaves becomes very noticeable. As in June, on the highest summits, snow sometimes falls but it does not normally lie for more than a few hours. Being the 'season of mists and mellow fruitfulness', and also lengthening shadows, this is the favourite time of the year for both photographers and artists. In an average year, the autumn colours are at their best in the second week of October. Again, also in an average year, in mid-October, one can expect the first air-frost, the first day with a maximum temperature in single figures, and the first dusting of snow on the fells.

By November, some attractions in the county have closed for the winter and the deteriorating weather, both colder and wetter, mean that it is best to make the most of early rather than late autumn.

This time of year has become increasingly popular for visitors and residents alike as recent autumns have produced excellent weather, with brilliant colours certainly rivalling those of New England.

It is an attractive time of the year to take a cruise on any of the larger lakes, perhaps more so than in the heart of summer. The scenery is probably at its best, with rich colour contrasts, while the weather has not usually cooled off enough to make such trips unpleasant.

What to expect weatherwise:

A generally calm autumn as opposed to a windy one can make all the difference as regards a brilliant display of autumn colours. Early gales can blow off most of the leaves before they have a chance to show their finery.

November sometimes produces a clear frosty spell, but on average is the least attractive month of the year.

N & NW winds – excellent visibility, mornings tending to be drier than afternoons. Cool nights, misty mornings. Frost from October onwards. Showery days rather than continuous rain. Hail, with a possibility of snow on the high fells, especially after the equinox.

E, NE & SE winds – rather uncommon. When they do occur, generally though not always a dry direction. More often than not, warm and hazy.

W & SW winds – can be wet and wild, but this is not a cold direction. On average, a higher strength than in Summer – look out for the equinoctial gales.

Suggestions to make the most of an **AUTUMN** day out:

Waterfalls – after a wet spell, this is a good time to visit waterfalls, as they are more attractive with bright sunlight and strong background colouring, with most of the leaves still on the trees. Many waterfalls are referred to as 'force', as in Aira Force. This is derived from the Viking word for a waterfall, i.e. 'foss' which is in common use in Norway and Iceland. It has no connection with power or energy. The original Norwegian spelling of 'foss' is still in use in a few places, for example in the Black Combe area.

Woodlands – the autumn colours are at their best, but go inland or to protected areas, as the stronger winds soon strip all the leaves in woodlands near the sea. Levens Park in the south of the county can be spectacular at this time of the year, as can Hutton-in-the-Forest, near Penrith.

Painting and Photography – extremely popular at this time of the year. This is reflected by the wealth of Art Galleries and artists materials shops.

Agricultural Shows – autumn being the traditional time to bring the sheep down from the fells before the onset of winter, it is also the time for a general get-together for the farmers.

Tarns – in many ways these are at their most attractive, especially on calm days giving colourful reflections. Tarn Hows near Coniston is popular and easily accessible.

Castles and Stately Homes – though some are open throughout the year, many close in mid-October.

44

In this part of the world blackberries do not mean BlackBerries! There are endless opportunities to find these delicious fruits. They are best picked early rather than late in the season, that is, late August into September. There are several subspecies, which ripen at different times which prolong the season.

WINTER: *December 1st to February 28th*

<u>General comments:</u> Of all the seasons, winter weather can be truly dreadful or absolutely magnificent. It can be at its worst in December and January, with very short hours of daylight, along with gales and torrential rain. Conversely, it can be at its best anytime during these two months, and even more so in February with cloudless skies and bright sunshine, a snow-covered landscape and sharp frosts.

However inviting they may look, now is NOT the time to venture on to the high fells, unless you are an experienced mountaineer. December, on average, is the wettest month of the year, January not quite so wet while February 'fill-dyke' does not usually live up to its name, and can be quite dry. It can also be a sunny month. On rare occasions the temperature can reach the mid-teens.

Compared with warm or cool summers, the difference between warm and cold winters is far greater. In a very mild winter, in coastal regions the grass still grows (slowly), and no snow at all will be recorded, e.g. the early 1930's. In a very severe winter snow can lie for several months and even the larger lakes can completely freeze over, e.g. 1895, 1947 and 1963.

In an average winter, Tarn Hows can be expected to more or less freeze over, while Rydal and Grasmere lakes will partially freeze, as will the head of Ullswater. The western lakes, such as Wastwater and Ennerdale (as far as the author can ascertain), have never been known to freeze completely, being too near the 'warm' waters of the Irish Sea.

If the weather is right, this is the time of year to take a short break, the restricted hours of daylight being compensated for by the roaring log fire at the end of the day.

More than in any other season, it is imperative that you obtain a highly accurate weather forecast.

If the weather is bad, there are several indoor attractions well worth visiting, which remain open throughout the year.

What to expect weatherwise:

N wind – contrary to what one might think, the very best direction. Under these conditions Cumbria lies under the 'rain or snow shadow' of the length of Scotland, and you can expect cloudless skies, with sunshine and sharp frosts. Visibility perfect!

NW wind – cold, with rain, hail sleet or snow showers to the west of the county and along the coast, especially from St. Bees to Walney, but otherwise clear and sunny, with excellent visibility.

E & NE wind – dry and hazy to the west of the county, but rain or snow to the east, especially in the Alston and Cross Fell area.

SE wind – can bring rain or snow to all areas.

S, SW & W winds – in general, a much milder direction, with rain or showers much heavier in the west, while the eastern part of Cumbria is far drier, especially the Eden Valley, as it lies in the 'rain shadow' of the Lake District fells.

Suggestions to make the most of a **WINTER** day out:

Keep it short! Winter anticyclones bring weather more or less stable for days at a time, often dry and sunny. Unfortunately, they are usually in very short supply. In general the weather is far more changeable than in the Summer months. Statistically, the most disturbed time of the year weather-wise is between Christmas and the New Year.

Waterfalls – after a wet spell, these are at their best, especially if Jack Frost has added his magic touch with the addition of some icicles.

Prehistoric stone circles – far more atmospheric at this time of the year, with mist and low sunlight. They still retain their mystery to a far greater extent than the much more famous Stonehenge. Castlerigg near Keswick is impressive, but the more remote Long Meg is even more so.

Tarns and small lakes – much more attractive than in the summer from an artistic or photographic standpoint, but painting outdoors in the colder weather is not for everyone.

Shopping and Craft Fairs – this is the time of year if the weather is really bad to visit indoor attractions, some of which remain open (such as 'Rheged' near Penrith) throughout the year. There are also many excellent Art Galleries and Museums in the district.

Winter Sports – Kendal Ski-Club runs a 'poma' lift high up on the slopes of Raise, near Helvellyn. It requires a very arduous steep climb to reach the bottom of the lift at 2,500 feet (762 metres) above sea level. Conditions can be excellent to appalling. Definitely one for the truly dedicated. When conditions are right, there are several opportunities in the Alston area, where temporary tows are set up. Provided the roads are clear, the region is reasonably accessible.

A far better bet when there is snow is to go sledging or tobogganing. Plenty of hills – plenty of opportunities!

At the time of writing there is no outdoor skating rink to be found in the area as are now being developed in many cities. In a severe cold snap some frozen tarns may look inviting, but many have underground springs and some have a build-up of methane gas underneath them – look but don't touch!

A round-up of some possible winter hazards:

Lost in the mist, and benighted on the fells? Check the weather forecast, and most importantly, *the hours of daylight.* Sudden formation of black ice, leading to road accidents – remember that ice can form on road surfaces, *even when the air temperature is above freezing.* Sudden formation of fog, drastically reducing visibility – this can happen especially in dips and hollows. *Visibility can change from several miles to a yard or two in a few minutes.* Severe gales – common in winter, especially on exposed sections of road, such as the higher parts of the M6. Wind-socks have recently been installed there.

Your guide to essential weather information

National radio and television forecasts are imprecise, superficial and often misleading. They also frequently omit Cumbria altogether.

Before making plans for the day, either

- make use of the reliable and detailed forecasts that can be found at 8.30 am, directly after Radio Cumbria news on FM 96.1.
- or **www.lake-district.gov.uk/weatherline**
- or telephone **0870 0550 575**

Especially on the high fells, weather conditions can change rapidly in a matter of minutes, but the above sources of information usually provide full details of any impending problems.

Cumbria and Climate Change

A book such as this would not be complete without some comments as regards 'global warming' or 'climate change'.

Human nature being what it is, there has always been a desire to know what the weather will be like tomorrow. Will there be a heat wave this summer, or possibly a freeze-up next winter?

Despite the millions of pounds spent on computers, along with thousands of satellite photographic images, weather forecasts for more than a week or two ahead are still largely guesswork. The truth is that there are so many factors that influence the weather and the climate, that to take one such factor in isolation, such as an increase in 'greenhouse gases' concentration is to be scientifically illiterate. Ocean currents, cloud cover, solar radiation, sunspots, volcanic dust in the atmosphere and at least a dozen other factors affect the weather and climate to a greater or lesser extent.

Certain facts are however clear:
- Without 'greenhouse gases' the earth would be in a deep freeze, *but*
- greenhouse gas concentrations rose steadily between approximately 1950 and 1975, *despite the fact that*

Aira Force – only appreciated with audio!

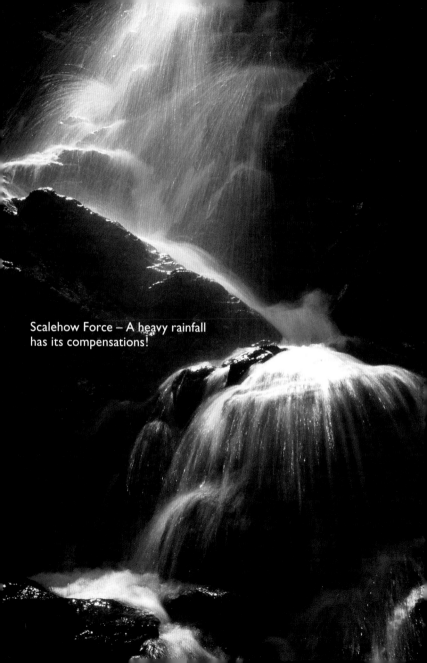

Scalehow Force – A heavy rainfall
has its compensations!

Man-made clouds

'Winter Sun, Coniston' (above), 'Spring Snows, Skiddaw' (below)

'Wind and Sun, Wastwater' Icebergs on the Kent Estuary

Sprinkling Tarn

The Brocken Spectre

Solar-powered boat on Coniston Water

Helvellyn weather observers

- Between these years the Earth's temperature *fell* slightly by just under 0.5°C leading to widespread forecasts by the 'experts' of an impending Ice Age.
- The Earth then warmed until 1998, but since then it has shown a slight cooling trend for the last ten years, accounting for the fact that the phrase 'global warming' is steadily falling into disuse, and is being replaced by 'climate change'.

Dire predictions have been made for the effects of climate change as regards Cumbria. A report appeared in June, 2008 entitled 'Low-carbon Lake District' which was discussed by over 100 delegates in Kendal. According to this report, temperature rises will cause forest fires and droughts, and woodlands will suffer more storm damage. Arctic char, a fish relict of the Ice Age found in the deeper lakes will die through suffocation. The changing weather will also increase to 30% the land suffering from extreme drought.

If these predictions do not appeal, then perhaps the following is a more likely scenario.

It could be that the weather and climate of Cumbria could easily take a turn for the worse. This could happen in a short space of time, in as little as a few years if the Gulf Stream failed or altered its course to the south. It is not generally realised that if Cumbria were to be moved to the same latitude in Canada it would lie in Hudson's Bay, far to the north of any of the major cities.

With the failure of the warm current, it would become practically uninhabitable, and after a few years glaciers would descend to the valley floors. Snow would fall throughout the year on all high ground, with the low ground resembling the arctic tundra of today.

There is ample evidence to show that such a climatic deterioration has happened at least once since the end of the last Ice Age, for a period of about five hundred years. The moraines indicating the termini of small glaciers are common throughout the district, formed well after the end of the last Ice Age.

Bearing the above contrary predictions in mind, perhaps those to be found in Horoscopes printed in the popular press, in the author's opinion, carry an equal degree of probability.

Cumbria is very fortunate in having very changeable and very unpredictable weather. When coupled with the march of seasonal changes, the result is that no two days are ever the same. Variety is said to be the spice of life, and the changing weather is certainly more appreciated by those familiar with the many parts of the world where the weather shows little or no variation for weeks on end.

It is very rare to experience extremely hot, and at the same time, humid summer days. Such days are common in many parts of the world, and can be extremely unpleasant. They can even be life-threatening for the elderly. Most summers pass without any such days. They do happen, but are rare – perhaps as rare as snow on the fells in June or September!

Marker stones at Levens Hall show previous flood levels. The highest occur when heavy rainfall inland results in a swollen river Kent. This then coincides with a south-west wind, low air pressure and a high tide.

PART THREE
Cumbria's weather in Art and Literature

It is not surprising that the capriciousness of the ever-changing weather, with its corresponding effects upon the varied landscapes of Cumbria, has long been celebrated by both writers and artists.

This small book can give but a taste of how writers and artists have been influenced by the weather. A visit to any of the numerous Art Galleries or bookshops in the region will soon show how the changing weather and changing seasons have affected their work.

The author has selected one writer, Norman Nicholson and one artist, William Heaton Cooper to illustrate the above points. Without this limitation, if the many writers and artists who have been drawn to the Lakes over the years were represented here, this section of the book would expand out of all proportion, and the tail would wag the dog! The following necessarily brief introduction to their writing and painting is to provide a 'taster' to their work which the reader can then explore further at leisure.

The writer and poet Norman Nicholson OBE, (1914 – 1987) was born and brought up in Millom in the south of the county, in the shadow of Black Combe. He spent all his life there, apart from a short spell in hospital, and, like the poet Wordsworth, developed a deep appreciation of nature and the weather in all its moods.

It could be thought that being restricted to one small area during his lifetime would be a disadvantage, but it is in fact a strength. By experiencing the weather and the seasons in all their moods in the Lake District, with the power of words he conveys to us in his poems that which artists can describe in their chosen medium. His work is best appreciated by reading his 'Collected Poems' (Faber & Faber).

A few lines will give a taste of his work:

'Cloud on Black Combe'
*'The air clarifies – rain
Has clocked off for the day'*

The meteorologist would say: 'It has been raining steadily in the warm sector of a passing depression, with poor visibility, but now following its passing, there is maritime polar air with excellent visibility'

He is a consummate master in his ability to portray in a few words the interaction of weather and landscape.

Similarly in his poem 'Haytiming' he includes the lines:

'That's the trouble with summer-
It's late so soon'

which brilliantly expresses the brief nature of the Cumbrian summer, which can fade into an early Autumn before it has really got going !

The artist William Heaton Cooper, (1903 – 1995) was born in Coniston, the son of the landscape painter Alfred Heaton Cooper. He was much more widely travelled than Norman Nicholson, having painted in Scotland, Norway, South America and the Swiss Alps. However, the bulk of his output does relate to the Lake District.

His work captures the ever-changing moods of the mountains. He states in one of his many books, 'The Tarns of Lakeland', that the best time of day to paint mountains is early morning or late evening, with mists arising from lakes and hills. Replacing the word 'paint' by the word 'photograph' in the previous sentence is still very sound advice.

A rough scientific analysis of his paintings shows that very few were painted in summer, and a disproportionately large number were painted in winter or early spring. In addition, as far as can be ascertained from the clear skies or type of cloud formations depicted, the wind, if any, was usually from the N or NW.

The weather in the peak summer months of July and August, the time most popular with visitors can be disappointing, and the light, according to the painter, frequently has a type of 'flat' quality inimicable to both painting and photography,

With the advent of high-quality digital cameras there are now many professional photographers in Cumbria who make the most of the opportunities provided by the interplay of the weather and the scenery.

Talented artists nevertheless seem able to capture that elusive 'something' that is the result of the subtle interaction of the weather and landscape.

During the summer and early autumn there are annual art exhibitions held in many towns and villages, while many galleries have year-round displays by local artists. The most prestigious annual exhibition is that of the Lake Artists Society, held from July through to September in Grasmere. This Society celebrated its Centenary in 2004.

A note as regards units:

Nowadays both metric and imperial units are in common use. Readers will probably be more familiar with one or the other sets of measurements, probably dependent upon their age! The author has adopted throughout the book the practise of quoting all the alternatives in everyday use, where appropriate.

Thus –'We had 38.1mm of rain last night' becomes 1.5 inches; 'It got up to 50^0F' yesterday becomes 10^0C; 'At last we are on top of Helvellyn at 950 metres, so we have reached 3,117 feet above sea level'.

Windspeeds are always quoted in miles per hour, as speeds measured in kilometres per hour have not yet entered the national consciousness!

How Cumbria's weather played an important role in the two nuclear accidents that have affected the county

At midnight on October 9th 1957, a fire broke out at an atomic reactor at Windscale (since renamed Sellafield, I wonder why?) on the west coast, which was not brought under control until the 12th of the month. This led to the escape of a large amount of radioactive material. At first there was a very light easterly drift at low level, with south westerly winds higher up. This resulted in some radioactive fallout in southwest Scotland. Early on October 10th the wind became north westerly pushing radioactivity to the south east where it was detected on the 11th at Leeds, London and Frankfurt. Even at this distance in time there are still allegations of cover-ups, and the wind directions depend to a certain extent as to which account you believe of the incident. For a time, milk was poured away, sales in Carlisle falling by 25%.

The nuclear accident at Chernobyl on April 26th 1986 resulted in a radioactive cloud passing over Cumbria, here the weather again playing a very important part. The exceptionally heavy rain especially in the west of the county resulted in radioactive contamination. Sheep from the fells were found to have received high doses, which, although it did not appear to affect the animals health in any way, the meat from those sheep was banned from the food chain. The radioactivity is not bound to the soil, so each spring the contamination is recirculated as sheep eat the new grass. However, when brought to the lowland pastures the sheep very rapidly lose any radioactive caesium 137, and in a few weeks are indistinguishable from sheep reared in parts of the country that have never been affected by fallout.

Fortunately no one in the U.K. is known to have lost their lives as a consequence of either of these incidents, unlike the many hundreds of miners who have died over the years in the now-defunct West Cumbrian coalfields.

This picture of the bay at St.Bees is the legendary landing place of the Irish saint Bega, who acquired the land shown in the photograph from the local Lord, as it was covered with snow on midsummer's day! (see page 9)

Acknowledgements:

Many thanks to my wife Otalia, and daughter Deborah, for editing the script and making a great job of hunting the apostrophes, and also deleting a surfeit of capital letters. Also to my daughter, Hilary for designing the cover.

Photographs:

There are very many books now on the market, superbly illustrating Cumbria's scenic landscape. However, this publication is unique in that the photographs have been specifically chosen to illustrate the effect that the changing weather has on the lakes, fells and valleys throughout the year.

Thanks are due to the many individuals who rummaged through their archives to provide the author with sometimes rare or even unique photographs.

The copyright of all photographs remains with the photographer, (apart from those taken in 1895, which are out of copyright). The author much appreciates illustrations contributed by the following; any not specifically mentioned here are the author's own work.

Cover:	Hilberry Designs Ltd.
	www.hilberrydesigns.co.uk
Summer Skiing:	Ian McVittie
Heaton Cooper paintings:	Heaton Cooper Studio Ltd.
	www.heatoncooper.co.uk
Kent Estuary Bore:	Arnold Price
Frozen River Kent:	Dennis Carefull
Windmills:	Susan Fletcher
Aira Force, Scalehow Force, Fairfield:	Trevor Brown
	www.trevorbrownphoto.co.uk
Helvellyn Weather Observers:	National Park Authority
The Brocken Spectre:	www.bridgehousegrasmere.co.uk
Sprinkling Tarn:	www.fenrunfellwalk.co.uk
Solar-powered boat:	Coniston Ferries
	conistonlaunch.co.uk
Flood Marker Stones	www.levenshall.co.uk
Morecambe Bay	David Ashcroft

Notes on the Photographs

Skiing in Summer

Though not remembered as being particularly cold, the winter of 1979 produced exceptional snowfall over all the high fells of Cumbria. Very large depths of snow built up, especially on the Pennines.

It was mid-August before Cross Fell again became completely snow-free.

These rare photographs show Ian McVittie of Penrith , watched by Mr. John Graham of Culgaith, skiing on Cross Fell above Penrith during July of that year.

Frozen Windermere 1895

113 years separate these two photos, taken from practically the same viewpoint. In 1895 excursion trains were run from major cities, including London, to Lakeside station to take advantage of the skating. This would not now be possible, as most of the branch line from the main line at Ulverston has been taken up. A short stretch still remains from Haverthwaite to Lakeside.

The last time Windermere was frozen to a similar extent was in 1963, though it has been partly frozen on several occasions since.

Tidal Bore, River Kent

It is quite remarkable how rare the phenomenon of a Tidal Bore is in the world, as a search on the Internet will quickly show. This photos shows the 'miniature tsunami' approaching Arnside from the south. It does not give a true impression of the speed of the advancing wave. This varies with the prevailing weather conditions, but in general it is not possible to outrun it.

Long Meg Sunset

This exceptionally rare photograph was taken at sunset on the shortest day of the year from the centre of the stone circle, in 1999, the last year of the twentieth century. This marked at least the *fourth* time 14 feet-high Long Meg, standing outside the circle has marked the passage of a Millennium. It also proves that the tilt of the earth's axis has remained remarkably constant over at least the last 4,000 years.

Long Meg Pillar

This sandstone monolith is badly eroded on its western side, indicating the direction of Cumbria's prevailing winds over the last forty or more centuries. Enigmatic prehistoric carvings are still to be seen on its sheltered eastern side.

Windswept Tree

This illustrates in a graphic way how persistently and strongly the west wind blows in coastal locations of Cumbria. The tree frames the distant Coniston Fells, the good visibility being typical of a northerly polar airstream.

After Sunset

Because windspeeds are far less inland than on the coast, wind generators must be sited high up in order to produce electricity, with, unlike hydro-power, damaging effects on the scenery. These three are about 1,000 feet above sea-level, near Kendal.

Thunderstorms

Viewed from inland looking westward towards the coast, in a northwest wind a seemingly never-ending stream of such clouds forms by convection over the (relatively) warm Irish Sea. As the air is forced upwards, such clouds tower many thousands of feet. As they move south, they sometimes join forces with those formed over the Wirral Peninsular. They then pass through the so-called 'Cheshire Gap', forming a cloud-street up to 200 miles long, clearly seen in satellite photographs.

Dunmail Moraines

These low rounded hills mark the terminus of a small glacier to the west of Dunmail Raise. They are thought to be due to a drastic change in the weather which occurred a few thousand years well after the end of the Ice Age, when the Gulf Stream, bringing warmth from Florida, failed for about 500 years. There are several other moraines in the district, all at about 800 feet above sea-level. Good examples are at the eastern end of Kirkstone Pass, and also in Mickleden, at the end of the valley of Great Langdale.

Langdale Moraines
Extensive moraines lie to the right-centre of this photograph, where green grass gives way to brown bracken. They were formed by a small glacier descending from Bowfell on the left of the picture

Man-made Clouds
Major air-routes to and from America and Canada pass over Cumbria, as well as short-haul routes to and from Scotland. Consequently it is very rare for there to be a time with no plane passing over Cumbria. In clear weather, it is not uncommon to see as many as 6 or 7 vapour trails in the sky at the same time. Under certain weather conditions, these dissipate very slowly, and spread out to form a blanket of cirrus clouds.

The photo illustrates this effect, the sky just out of the picture continuing to be blue and cloudless.

This high cloud blanket must have an effect on Cumbria's weather, probably cooling it as some of the sun's rays are reflected back into space. However, it can also be argued that the cloud blanket traps heat that would otherwise be radiated into space, leading to a warming effect.

Aira Force
Only fully appreciated with audio! 'Force' here is cognate with the Norwegian 'Foss'

Scalehow Force
A heavy rainfall has its compensations !

William Heaton Cooper paintings
These three paintings by William Heaton Cooper (1903 – 1995) illustrate perfectly how an artist can sometimes capture the evanescent moods of the weather which can frequently escape the professional photographer.

'Winter Sun, Coniston'
Here, the west wind is forced upwards over Dow Crags and Coniston Old Man. In doing so it cools and produces a stream of clouds away to the east. In the far distance the same effect can be seen over the snows of the Helvellyn range.

The chill in the air can be felt just by looking at the picture.

'Spring Snows, Skiddaw'
This painting, with Derwentwater in the foreground, in which the mountain Skiddaw is reflected illustrates the formation of cumulus shower clouds in a cold north-westerly air flow.

Such clouds often form a seemingly endless succession, known as 'streets'. On the top right of the picture is the base of one passing away, while the next one in line is to the right of Skiddaw summit. The following one can be seen forming on the left of the picture.

Wispy clouds on the top left herald the approach of another weather system. The picture can of course be appreciated without any meteorological knowledge, but the fact that all the clouds are 'in exactly the right places' adds greatly to the harmony and integrity of a great painting.

Wind and Sun, Wastwater
The north-easterly wind is here producing a cloud-cap or 'helm' over the summit of Great Gable in the centre of the picture. The fierce downdraft to the right is well illustrated and is a textbook example of the Helm Wind, better known on Cross Fell, which blows down to the Eden Valley.

The Brocken Spectre
This eerie appearance was captured one winter's day on Blencathra, east of Keswick, only the fell-tops being clear, and the valleys remaining shrouded in low cloud.

Icebergs on the Kent Estuary
Frosts are sometimes sharp enough to produce small icebergs in Morecambe Bay, which can then be piled on one another by the tide. As this book was going to press, (February 2009), the cold weather had produced some small ice-floes near Arnside.

Sprinkling Tarn
This small tarn, lying near Great Gable and Great End, in a wet year receives over 200 inches of rain. (more than 5,000 mms). It is near the hub of a wheel , the spokes of which are the lakes. This means that

whatever direction the wind blows, the air is forced up one of the valleys that converge on the area, cools and deposits rain or snow.

Because of this peculiar topography, the central mountainous area has a rainfall comparable with the notoriously wet south-west coast of New Zealand, in the Fox and Franz Joseph Glacier area.

Solar-powered Boat
This launch, which operates on Coniston Water during the summer months, illustrates how, even in Cumbria's rather cloudy climate, sufficient electricity can be produced by the sun to make its operation viable. The roof is covered with panels that produce electricity. These charge the batteries even when the launch is not in operation, so giving an energy boost on cloudy days.

Helvellyn weather observers
High on the mountain, these two observers compare notes, taking readings of temperature and wind velocity. Their readings are made public and can be accessed via www.lake-district.gov.uk/weatherline. Weather permitting, photographs are also available of fell-top conditions. At the time of writing, this National Park service operates throughout the winter months.

The above pictures have been selected not so much for their technical quality but for their capability of illustrating particular aspects of Cumbria's weather.

With the advent of high quality digital photography, there are now many excellent illustrated books which do justice to Cumbria's scenery.

There are also many web-cams throughout the district giving up-to-the-minute pictures of the fells and weather conditions.

They are not listed here individually as they are not always operational, but a 'Google' search will soon find some.

Cumbria's Weather & Cumbria's Climate

Nowadays the terms 'weather' and 'climate' are frequently, but incorrectly, used interchangeably.

Climate: The dictionary describes 'climate' as 'the long term prevalent weather conditions of an area, determined by latitude, position relative to oceans or continents, altitude etc.'

Weather: This is defined as ' the day-to-day meteorological conditions, especially temperature, cloudiness and rainfall affecting a specific place.

'Climate change' is now constantly in the news – in fact it is now part of a Government Minister's portfolio. Thus we hear that the latest storm, freeze-up, blizzard or heat-wave is all part of 'climate change'. This is, of course, sheer nonsense. Only by comparing the weather over a long period of time in the past with the weather over a similar period of time as currently being measured is it possible to make meaningful statements about climate change.

There has never been any period in which the climate has *not* changed. It is constantly altering in an entirely predictable way. Because the orbit of the earth is an ellipse and not a true circle, and the earth's axis is tilted, Cumbria is actually nearest the sun in January and furthest away in July, so winters are warmer and summers are cooler than they would otherwise be. Don't believe me? Focus an image of the sun on a piece of card in June and in December (if it's shining!) and see which makes the biggest circle! In the course of time, the position will be reversed, and consequently the climate will change. Don't hold your breath though – these slow changes take place over thousands of years.

So what is the scientific evidence for climate change in Cumbria?

Evidence for a past colder climate

Since the end of the last Ice-age, an accurate picture has been built up over the years of the climate of Cumbria. This has been achieved by the study of sediments from the bottom of lakes and tarns. An analysis of pollen grains show clearly the changing patterns of tree growth. What should concern us is the fact that the climate, hardly different from today, all at once underwent a sudden dramatic cooling. The temperature fell about 10^0C in as many years Some scientists assert that this happened within *less* than ten years, though this is certainly open to argument.

The result was a mini Ice-age, with glaciers descending to only 800 feet /250 metres or so above sea-level. (See illustrations on colour pages)

After a period of about five hundred years, they vanished as quickly as they had formed as the climate swung back to 'normal'.

A possible explanation for this climate change is that it was the result of global warming. As the earth warmed up after the last major Ice-age, melt-water from Canadian ice-sheets flooded into the Atlantic. This fresh cold water, being less dense than the Gulf Stream, lay on top of it and effectively cut off its warming influence. After a few hundred years, the Gulf Stream suddenly re-exerted its influence, and normal service was resumed.

Should this happen again, the consequences would be catastrophic, and Cumbria would become more or less uninhabitable.

More recently, there is abundant written evidence from the 17th and 18th centuries that the climate then was colder than today, with much more severe winters. This appears to have been connected with the activity of the sun, as this cooling coincided with an absence of sunspots.

Evidence for a past warmer climate

It is quite clear that the climate of what was to become Cumbria was considerably warmer than today about 4 to 5,000 years ago.

Tree trunks preserved in peat can be found on the fells at altitudes where they could not possibly now grow. There are also numerous remains of prehistoric settlements in very exposed positions, up to 1,500 feet / 500 metres above sea-level. Just north of the border, in Dumfries and Galloway, there are the remains of prehistoric cultivation terraces on north- facing slopes well over 1,000 feet / 350 metres above sea-level.

Further proof of this warmer period comes from the remains of buried forests off-shore in the Barrow area. They were supposedly drowned as the sea-level rose as the arctic ice melted with the increased warmth.

It is human nature to want to know the future. For thousands of years countless methods of divination have been tried, from studying the entrails of slaughtered animals to the form of the lines on the human palm. Even in this rational and scientific age, many readers turn first to the page with the horoscopes, in their daily newspaper or magazine.

Computer modelling has now taken over to predict the climate for sometimes decades ahead. As with horoscopes, successful predictions are made public, but failures take a back seat.

As far as the writer is aware, no computer model anywhere predicted the complete lack of global warming since it peaked in 1998. In fact the last decade has seen a slight global cooling.

Leaving aside the question of whether global warming or global cooling is a reality, what would be their effect on Cumbria?

A warming of the climate:

The effects of a warmer climate would be largely beneficial, as far less fossil fuel would be required for domestic and industrial heating. The demand for electricity would fall, where at present it is used for heating. In addition, a longer growing season would be a boon to farmers. A lack of frost would benefit fruit growers, and courgettes and tomatoes could possibly be grown commercially outside, and not under glass.

Even if rainfall diminished substantially, water shortages would not be critical, as many regions of the world cope well with far less than the present average rainfall in Cumbria.

An aesthetic disadvantage would be that a lack of snow on the fells in winter would detract from their scenic appeal, but it is difficult to think of any major disadvantage.

A cooling of the climate:

The effects of a cooler climate would be largely negative. More fossil fuel would be needed, and there would be an increased demand for electricity.

Crops would also be affected, with a much shorter growing season.

If the cooling were to be prolonged and severe, a population drift southwards would be likely.

With heavy and persistent snowfalls, a possible advantage of this type of climatic change would be the development of a Winter Sports industry. The topography of Cumbria is ideally suited for the establishment of such activities.

In conclusion, taken as a whole, a warming trend, as long as it is not too rapid or severe, would be infinitely preferable to the opposite.